Monsters One to Ten

By Emily Thompson
Illustrated by Tom Leigh

LEVEL **READING LEVEL Pre 1** READER

Published by Bendon Publishing International, Inc. All rights reserved.
Printed in Haining, Zhejiang, China.

The BENDON name is a trademark of Bendon Publishing International, Inc.
Ashland, Ohio 44805. 1-888-5-BENDON. bendonpub.com
No part of this book may be reproduced or copied in any form without written permission
from the copyright owner. 81320-TG F 0214

One tire…

...makes a fun swing.

Two hands...

...make a yummy lunch.

Three snowballs...

...make a cold snowman.

Four letters...

...make Elmo's name.

Five music makers...

...make a jazzy band.

Six friends make a tall tower.

Seven stars make
the Big Dipper.

Eight patches...

...make a comfy quilt.

Nine players make
a baseball team.

Ten monsters...

...make a big mess!